W◯zone

discovering
God's
wonderful
world

Lab Book

This booklet belongs to

....

© Scripture Union 2019

First published 2019

ISBN 978 1 78506 790 7

Scripture Union
Trinity House, Opal Court, Opal Drive,
Fox Milne, Milton Keynes, MK15 0DF
email: info@scriptureunion.org.uk
www.scriptureunion.org.uk

The right of Alex Taylor to be identified
as the author of this work has been
asserted by him in accordance with the
Copyright, Designs and Patents Act 1988.

Scripture quotations are from the
Contemporary English Version published
by HarperCollins*Publishers* © 1991, 1992,
1995 American Bible Society. Used by
permission.

British Library Cataloguing-in-
Publication Data
A catalogue record of this book is
available from the British Library.

Printed and bound in Malta by Melita
Press
Cover and internal design by
kwgraphicdesign
Internal illustrations by Tim Charnick

Scripture Union is an international
Christian charity working with churches
in more than 130 countries. Thank you
for purchasing this book. Any profits
from this book support SU in England
and Wales to bring the good news of
Jesus Christ to children, young people
and families and to enable them to
meet God through the Bible and prayer.

Find out more about our work and
how you can get involved at:
● www.scriptureunion.org.uk
  (England and Wales)
● www.suscotland.org.uk (Scotland)
● www.suni.co.uk (Northern Ireland)
● www.scriptureunion.org (USA)
● www.su.org.au (Australia)

Wonder Zone has been produced
in collaboration with The Faraday
Institute for Science and Religion.
The Faraday Institute is an
interdisciplinary research and
communication enterprise linked to
the University of Cambridge.

This project and publication were made
possible through the support of a grant
from the John Templeton Foundation.
The opinions expressed in this
publication are those of the author(s)
and do not necessarily reflect the views
of the John Templeton Foundation.

Welcome to your Lab Book!

Here's where you can record all your discoveries and findings as you come to **Wonder Zone**. There's space for experiments and to write down everything you find out about God too. You'll also discover that you can be friends with Jesus!

The Bible is split into two sections (the Old Testament and the New Testament). These two testaments are split into books (the Old Testament has 39 books, the New Testament has 27). The books are split into chapters (the biggest book, Psalms, has 150 chapters!) and those chapters are split into verses (the longest chapter is Psalm 119 with 176 verses!). Sometimes you'll see a Bible verse written like this: Psalm 139:14. Here is how you tell which verse to read:

Psalm 139 : 14

Psalm means we need to look for the **Bible book of Psalms**. If you are not sure where this is, look for the contents page near the beginning of the Bible.

139 means we need to look for the big number 139; we call it **chapter 139**.

14 means we need to look for the little number 14; we call it **verse 14**.

This **Scientist**

Some people like living things, some like explosions. Some people love space travel, some love coding. Scientists are passionate about lots of things!

What do you like? Write or draw your ideas here!

I really like...

I'd love to find out about...

Your **ID** card

Here's your ID card for **Wonder Zone.**

Draw a picture of yourself
as a Scientist and fill in your
details on the card. Or dress up
and ask someone to take your
picture – and stick it in here!

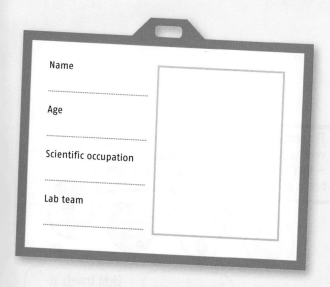

Name

....

Age

....

Scientific occupation

....

Lab team

....

The **fun** of discovery

Discovering new things is what studying science is all about. What have you discovered recently?

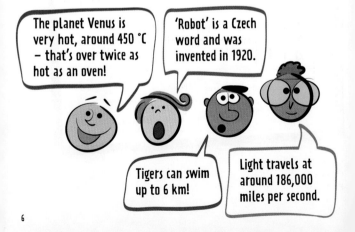

The planet Venus is very hot, around 450 °C – that's over twice as hot as an oven!

'Robot' is a Czech word and was invented in 1920.

Tigers can swim up to 6 km!

Light travels at around 186,000 miles per second.

EXPERIMENT 1
Discover the words

Can you find all these words in this tricky wordsearch?

S	A	U	G	A	T	E	C	H	C
K	N	R	E	S	E	A	R	C	H
M	I	C	R	O	S	C	O	P	E
L	M	Z	F	D	T	H	B	P	M
Y	A	I	U	E	C	X	O	L	I
F	L	B	N	L	L	R	T	A	S
E	X	P	E	R	I	M	E	N	T
W	B	I	O	L	O	G	Y	E	R
A	O	T	N	Q	R	J	H	T	Y
V	F	A	R	E	S	U	L	T	S

ANIMAL   FUN   PLANET   TECH
BIOLOGY   LAB   RESEARCH   TEST
CHEMISTRY   LIGHT   RESULTS
EXPERIMENT   MICROSCOPE   ROBOT

7

EXPERIMENT ①
The very wise king

Read the story about Solomon and his choice to know more!

Underline anything that you like and draw a circle around things that surprise you.

. . . .

5 One night while Solomon was in Gibeon, the Lord God appeared to him in a dream and said, "Solomon, ask for anything you want, and I will give it to you."

6 Solomon answered: My father David, your servant, was honest and did what you commanded. You were always loyal to him, and you gave him a son who is now king. **7** Lord God, I'm your servant, and you've made me king in my father's place. But I'm very young and know so little about being a leader. **8** And now I must rule your chosen people, even though there are too many of them to count.

9 Please make me wise and teach me the difference between right and wrong. Then I will know how to rule your people. If you don't, there is no way I could rule this great nation of yours.

10-11 God said: Solomon, I'm pleased that you asked for this. You could have asked to live a long time or to be rich. Or you could have asked for your enemies to be destroyed. Instead, you asked for wisdom to make right decisions. **12** So I'll make you wiser than anyone who has ever lived or ever will live.

13 I'll also give you what you didn't ask for. You'll be rich and respected as long as you live, and you'll be greater than any other king. **14** If you obey me and follow my commands, as your father David did, I'll let you live a long time.

1 Kings 3:5–14

. . . .

EXPERIMENT 1
Know more about knowing!

The Bible is full of verses saying how great it is to get more knowledge, understanding and wisdom!

Crack the code to complete these verses.

Clue: 1=A, 2=B, 3=C

"If you have _7_ _15_ _15_ _4_ sense, instruction will help you to have even _2_ _5_ _20_ _20_ _5_ _18_ sense. And if you live _18_ _9_ _7_ _8_ _20_, education will help you to know even _13_ _15_ _18_ _5_ " (Proverbs 9:9).

. . . .

"It's much _2_ _5_ _20_ _20_ _5_ _18_ to be wise and sensible than to be _18_ _9_ _3_ _8_ " (Proverbs 16:16).

. . . .

"Everyone with _7_ _15_ _15_ _4_ sense wants to _12_ _5_ _1_ _18_ _14_ " (Proverbs 18:15).

. . . .

What do you like about discovering new things?

9

EXPERIMENT 1
Experiment at home!

Continue the joy of discovery with this slimy experiment you can do at home!

You will need:
- cornflour
- water
- food colouring (optional)
- bowl
- spoon

Put a few spoonsful of cornflour in the bowl and keep adding water until you get a thick slimy paste. If you want to, colour your slime with a few drops of food colouring.

What happens if you try to stir the slime slowly?

What happens if you try to stir the slime really fast?

What happens if you hit the slime with the back of your spoon?

Anything that is gas or liquid is called a fluid. Milk is a fluid that has low viscosity (it pours easily). Golden syrup has high viscosity (it's tricky to pour). This slime doesn't behave like normal fluids. When you apply pressure to it, it becomes thicker. This is called a "shear-thickening" or "non-Newtonian" fluid!

The **wonders** of the universe

The closest star to the sun is called Proxima Centauri. It's 4.22 light years away! With the twin stars of Alpha Centauri A and B, it forms the nearest star system to us. It's still a long way away though!

The universe is bigger than you can imagine, but do you know the names of our nearest neighbours in space? Here's the solar system – can you name the planets?

Pluto used to be the ninth planet, but in 2006, the International Astronomical Union redefined what a planet was. And now Pluto is a "dwarf planet".

Many scientists think there may be another planet beyond Neptune! Nobody has seen it yet, so they don't know for certain...

EXPERIMENT 2
Light up the Bible!

Here is our Bible passage for today. Can you make it look amazing with pictures inspired by the words?

Draw, doodle and write all around the psalm!

• •

1 Our Lord and Ruler,
your name is wonderful
everywhere on earth!
You let your glory be seen
in the heavens above.

2 With praises from children
and from tiny infants,
you have built a fortress.
It makes your enemies silent,
and all who turn against you
are left speechless.

3 I often think of the heavens
your hands have made,
and of the moon and stars
you put in place.

⁴ Then I ask, "Why do you care
about us humans?
Why are you concerned
for us weaklings?"

⁵ You made us a little lower
than you yourself,
and you have crowned us
with glory and honour.

⁶ You let us rule everything
your hands have made
And you put all of it
under our power—

⁷ the sheep and the cattle,
and every wild animal,

⁸ the birds in the sky,
the fish in the sea,
and all ocean creatures.

⁹ Our Lord and Ruler,
your name is wonderful
everywhere on earth!

Psalm 8

EXPERIMENT 2
Map your mind!

The universe is so big and we are so small. But we are special to God! How do you feel about that?

Use this mind map to write or draw all your thoughts, all the things you want to ask and anything you've discovered today. Here are two thoughts to get you started.

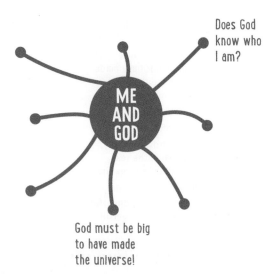

Does God know who I am?

ME AND GOD

God must be big to have made the universe!

Don't agree with these suggestions?
Cross them out and write or draw your own ideas!

EXPERIMENT 2
Experiment at home!

On a clear night, go outside with an adult and look up into the sky.

What things can you see?

Draw some of them here:

If you can get hold of some binoculars or even a telescope, look through those. What can you see now? Can you see any planets?

Draw the moon or those planets here:

If possible, ask the adult with you if they can download a stargazing app on their phone. There are some free ones available, such as SkyView or Star Walk 2 (there's a children's version of this one). Hold the phone up to the sky and you can identify what you can see! What's your favourite thing?

Draw it here:

EXPERIMENT ③
The **colours** of the rainbow

Do you know the colours of the rainbow?

Colour in the correct colours on this diagram!

Do you know what causes a rainbow? Chat in your Lab to discover how!

EXPERIMENT 3
Light up the difference!

Look at these two pictures. Can you spot the ten differences between the two?

What's the difference between the plants? Why do you think they're different?

EXPERIMENT 3
The gift of light!

Read this Bible story and fill in the blank faces to show how the characters might be feeling!

¹ As Jesus walked along, he saw a man who had been blind since birth. ² Jesus' disciples asked, "Teacher, why was this man born blind? Was it because he or his parents sinned?"

³ "No, it wasn't!" Jesus answered. "But because of his blindness, you will see God work a miracle for him. ⁴ As long as it is day, we must do what the one who sent me wants me to do. When night comes, no one can work. ⁵ While I am in the world, I am the light for the world."

⁶ After Jesus said this, he spit on the ground. He made some mud and smeared it on the man's eyes. ⁷ Then he said, "Go and wash off the mud in Siloam Pool." The man went and washed in Siloam, which means "One Who Is Sent." When he had washed off the mud, he could see.

¹³⁻¹⁴ The day when Jesus made the mud and healed the man was a Sabbath. So the people took the man to the Pharisees. ¹⁵ They asked him how he was able to see, and he answered, "Jesus made some mud and smeared it on my eyes. Then after I washed it off, I could see."

¹⁶ Some of the Pharisees said, "This man Jesus doesn't come from God. If he did, he would not break the law of the Sabbath."

The disciples

The blind m

The Pharisees

Others asked, "How could someone who is a sinner work such a miracle?"

²⁴ The leaders called the man back and said, "Swear by God to tell the truth! We know that Jesus is a sinner."

²⁵ The man replied, "I don't know if he is a sinner or not. All I know is that I used to be blind, but now I can see!"

²⁶ "What did he do to you?" the Jewish leaders asked. "How did he heal your eyes?"

²⁷ The man answered, "I have already told you once, and you refused to listen. Why do you want me to tell you again? Do you also want to become his disciples?"

²⁸ The leaders insulted the man and said, "You are his follower! We are followers of Moses. ²⁹ We are sure that God spoke to Moses, but we don't even know where Jesus comes from."

³⁰ "How strange!" the man replied. "He healed my eyes, and yet you don't know where he comes from. ³¹ We know that God listens only to people who love and obey him. God doesn't listen to sinners. ³² And this is the first time in history that anyone has ever given sight to someone born blind. ³³ Jesus could not do anything unless he came from God."

³⁹ Jesus told him [the man who was blind], "I came to judge the people of this world. I am here to give sight to the blind and to make blind everyone who can see."

The blind man

⁴⁰ When the Pharisees heard Jesus say this, they asked, "Are we blind?"

⁴¹ Jesus answered, "If you were blind, you would not be guilty. But now that you claim to see, you will keep on being guilty."

John 9:1–41 (but not all of it!)
. . . .

The Pharisees

Light for the world

In John 8:12, Jesus said:

I am the light for the world! Follow me, and you won't be walking in the dark. You will have the light that gives life.

What do you think he meant?

Write or draw your ideas here!

What do the other Scientists in your Lab think?

EXPERIMENT 3
Experiment at home!

You will need:
- a jar
- some water
- some milk
- a torch

Fill your jar two-thirds full with water and then drop in half a teaspoon of milk. Stir it around and put the lid on the jar (so you don't make a mess if you knock it over!). Find a room in your house that you can make dark (or wait until evening) and shine your torch at the side of the jar. Look at the jar from the front. What colour does the milky water go?

Then shine the torch at the back of the jar and look at it from the front. What colour is the milky water now?

Why do you think that happens? Can you find out?

Ask an adult to help you investigate on the internet!

Life on Earth

All Christians agree that God created everything and that he loves it all. That's what the Bible tells us. Science can be seen as a gift from God to help us understand more details, like *how* life on Earth developed.

Some people have different ideas about exactly how and when this happened. That's OK, and it can be really interesting to talk about.

Scientists – including those who are Christians – have put together clues from the world around us to produce this exciting story of how they think life on Earth developed.

There are lots of interesting questions to ask about how God made everything, and how our scientific discoveries fit with what we learn from the Bible about God as Creator. Some

people believe different things about this, but all Christians agree that the most important thing is to get to know who Jesus is and how much he loves us. That doesn't ever change!

If you know someone with different ideas to you, why not talk together, see what's the same, what's different, and enjoy investigating how God made his wonderful creation?

About 4.5 billion years ago
The Earth is formed

About 3.7 billion years ago
The first life appears, called
prokaryotic cells
(like bacteria!)

About 570 million years ago
The first arthropods (you can
still see arthropods now,
things like insects, spiders,
centipedes and crabs)

**About 530 million
years ago**
The first fish

**About
200,000
years ago**
The first
humans

You!

**About 200 million
years ago**
The first
mammals

**bout 475 million
ars ago**
e first land plants (followed 90
llion years later by the first forests)

Humans have only been around
for 0.004% of the Earth's life!

25

The **creatures** of the world

Do you know lots of birds? Take a look out of the window and count all the birds you can see.

Record everything in this table.

Name of bird	Number of birds

You could even draw pictures of the birds you see! If you can't see any birds, get outside and see how many different insects and spiders you can find!

EXPERIMENT 4
What's that?

Can you tell what these animals are? How many can you identify?

Find the answers on page 48.

1

....

2

....

3

....

4

....

5

....

6

....

EXPERIMENT 4
You are known!

God, who made the whole world, made you too. And he cares about you.

Read through this psalm and draw emojis around it to show how the words make you feel.

¹ You have looked deep
into my heart, Lord,
and you know all about me.
² You know when I am resting
or when I am working,
and from heaven
you discover my thoughts.

³ You notice everything I do
and everywhere I go.
⁴ Before I even speak a word,
you know what I will say,
⁵ and with your powerful arm
you protect me
from every side.
⁶ I can't understand all of this!
Such wonderful knowledge
is far above me.

Psalm 139:1–6

¹³ You are the one
who put me together
inside my mother's body,
¹⁴ and I praise you
because of
the wonderful way
you created me.
Everything you do is marvellous!
Of this I have no doubt.

¹⁵ Nothing about me
is hidden from you!
I was secretly woven together
deep in the earth below,
¹⁶ but with your own eyes
you saw
my body being formed.
Even before I was born,
you had written in your book
everything I would do.

¹⁷ Your thoughts are far beyond
my understanding,
much more than I
could ever imagine.
¹⁸ I try to count your thoughts,
but they outnumber the grains
of sand on the beach.
And when I awake,
I will find you nearby.

Psalm 139:13–18

EXPERIMENT 4
Write your own psalm!

Do you think you can write a psalm about God, creation and you?

Fill in the gaps with words or pictures!

God, you are   !

You made   and

it is   .

When I see   it

makes me feel   .

God, you are   !

The   is

full of   .

Being in your creation

makes me feel   .

God, you are   !

You made me and know

me and that is   .

You are with me all the

time and so I   .

God, you are   !

EXPERIMENT 4
Experiment at home

Take your *Lab Book* and a pencil (and some crayons or pencil crayons, if you have them) and go outside. Look in your garden or a local park and see what mini-beasts you can find!

Can you find a beast that crawls? Draw it here!

Can you find a beast that flies? Draw it here!

Can you find a beast that slithers? Draw it here!

Can you find a beast that runs? Draw it here!

When you get home, see if you can identify what you've found. And if other Scientists have done this experiment, then compare your results with theirs!

EXPERIMENT 5
The programming of robots

If you could design a robot, what would it be like? What would it do?

Draw your robot here!

EXPERIMENT 5
Choices, choices

Are you good at making choices?
What would you do in these situations?

You see a woman drop £5 out of her purse. Do you:

a Pick it up and give it back to her?

b Wait until she walks off, then pick it up and keep it?

c Do nothing?

Your friend lends you their robot toy, but you break it. Do you:

a Lie and say it was already broken?

b Blame the dog?

c Own up and offer to get a new one?

Your friend loses their packed lunch at school. Do you:

a Share your lunch with them?

b Throw your lunch away so that no one has any food?

c Eat all your lunch in front of them, making loud "Nom nom" noises?

EXPERIMENT 5
The lost son

Read this story and decide what you would have done at each point!

....

11 Jesus also told them another story:

Once a man had two sons. **12** The younger son said to his father, "Give me my share of the property." So the father divided his property between his two sons.

What did the son choose to do? What would you have done if you were the father?

13 Not long after that, the younger son packed up everything he owned and left for a foreign country, where he wasted all his money in wild living. **14** He had spent everything, when a bad famine spread through that whole land.

Soon he had nothing to eat.

15 He went to work for a man in that country, and the man sent him out to take care of his pigs. **16** He would have been glad to eat what the pigs were eating, but no one gave him a thing.

What would you have done if you were the son?

17 Finally, he came to his senses and said, "My father's workers have plenty to eat, and here I am, starving to death! **18** I will go to my father and say to him, 'Father, I have sinned against God in heaven and against you. **19** I am no longer good enough to be

called your son. Treat me like one of your workers.'"

20 The younger son got up and started back to his father. But when he was still a long way off, his father saw him and felt sorry for him. He ran to his son and hugged and kissed him.

What choice did the father make? Was it the right one?

21 The son said, "Father, I have sinned against God in heaven and against you. I am no longer good enough to be called your son."

22 But his father said to the servants, "Hurry and bring the best clothes and put them on him. Give him a ring for his finger and sandals for his feet. **23** Get the best calf and prepare it, so we can eat and celebrate. **24** This son of mine was dead, but has now come back to life. He was lost and has now been found." And they began to celebrate.

25 The older son had been out in the field. But when he came near the house, he heard the music and dancing. **26** So he called one of the servants over and asked, "What's going on here?"

27 The servant answered, "Your brother has come home safe and sound, and your father ordered us to kill the best calf." **28** The older brother got so angry that he would not even go into the house.

If you were the older brother, what would you have done?

His father came out and begged him to go in. **29** But he said to his father, "For years I have worked for you like a slave and have always obeyed you. But you have never even given me a little goat, so that I could give a dinner for my friends. **30** This other son of yours wasted your money on prostitutes. And now that he has come home, you ordered the best calf to be killed for a feast."

31 His father replied, "My son, you are always with me, and everything I have is yours. **32** But we should be glad and celebrate! Your brother was dead, but he is now alive. He was lost and has now been found."

Do you think the older brother went into the party?

Luke 15:11–32

• •

What about you?

The younger son made some bad choices, but then he made a good one at the end. What about you?

God is waiting to throw his arms around you, just like the father in the story. How does this make you feel?

Circle the words that are the best match for you.

Happy

Relieved

Excited

Bored

Nervous

Sad

Terrible

Great

Can't see the word you want? Write it in!

EXPERIMENT 5
Experiment at home

Make your own bristlebot!

You will need
- a toothbrush
- a 6 mm vibrating motor
- an LR44 cell battery
- some double-sided sticky tape

You'll need an adult to help you with this. You can get a motor online or from a model-making shop. The batteries are available in shops and supermarkets.

It's a bit complicated to explain how to do this in *Lab Book*, so ask an adult to help you find a video online to show you what to do!

If you want to, you could stick some googly eyes on your bristlebot and give it a name!

How does the bot move about? Write or draw it here!

Learn and remember verse

Can you use your scientific skills to solve the code and uncover the *Learn and remember* verse?

"R   KIZRHV   BLF
_   _____   ___

YVXZFHV   LU   GSV
_____   __   ___

DLMWVIUFO   DZB
_____   ___

BLF   XIVZGVW   NV.
___   _____   __

VEVIBGSRMT
_____

BLF   WL   RH
___   __   __

NZIEVOOLFH!
_____

LU   GSRH   R   SZEV
__   ____   _   ____

ML   WLFYG."
__   _____

KHZON 139:14
_____

Codebreaker

A	B	C	D	E	F	G	H	I	J	K	L	M
Z	Y	X	W	V	U	T	S	R	Q	P	O	N
N	O	P	Q	R	S	T	U	V	W	X	Y	Z
M	L	K	J	I	H	G	F	E	D	C	B	A

Test it out!

Do you know lots about different sciences? Test your brain with this quiz! If you don't know the answers, try to find out!

1 What are the common names for these chemical formulae?

A NaCl

....

B H_2O

....

C C

....

D $NaHCO_3$

....

2 What's the name of the dwarf planet beyond Neptune?

....

3 What is the coloured part of your eye called? (And what colour are your eyes?)

....

4 Can you tell what these animals are by the pattern on their skin?

A ....

B ....

C ....

D ....

5 Can you name a voice assistant (on a phone or speaker device)?

....

You and God

Now you have discovered some amazing things about the world around you from the very big to the very small! What do you think about God who made it all?

Circle what is closest to what you think.

I try to trust in God, but **I need some help.**

I think **I'm interested**, but not just yet.

I'm already **following** Jesus!

I am **not really bothered**, thanks.

I would **love to trust** God and live his way.

Talk to your Researcher or Lab Technicians about what you have circled. They would love to know and to help you, if you want.

God's plan

God has created a world which he loves and there is so much good in it.

He made land and sea, plants and animals, and humans who were a bit like him. He wanted these people to be his friends.

But humans decided that they didn't want to be God's friend. They decided they'd rather do what they wanted – and that meant being mean to each other, hurting each other and turning their back on God.

And yet God never stopped loving humans. He looked after them, even though they ignored him. He sent them messengers to tell them how much he loved them. But lots of them still ignored him.

He promised his people that he would send a special Saviour, someone who would be king for ever and who would mend the friendship between God and humans. A man called John called this Saviour the "Word".

¹ In the beginning was the one who is called the **Word**. The **Word** was with God and was truly God.

² From the very beginning the **Word** was with God.

³ And with this **Word**, God created all things. Nothing was made without the **Word**.

¹⁴ The **Word** became a human being and lived here with us. We saw his true glory, the glory of the only Son of the Father. From him all the kindness and all the truth of God have come down to us.

John 1:1-3,14

That Saviour, the **Word**, is Jesus!

The **greatest** discovery

You've discovered so much at **Wonder Zone**, about the world around you, about space, about life on earth... and also about God and what it means to be his friend.

In fact, that's what the Bible is all about – the story of how much God loves his people and wants to be friends with them once more. The Bible tells us how God sent his Son Jesus – God's special Saviour – to live with us and show us how to love God.

And then some people who didn't like Jesus put him to death. But that wasn't the end – Jesus came alive again! (Check out Mark chapters 14, 15 and 16 in the Bible.) Jesus died to take all the punishment we deserve. And so we can be friends with God again.

Millions of people all around the world are part of this plan and are friends with God. God's powerful Holy Spirit is helping

them. Have you joined in the investigations?

If you want to do that, just tell him. If you're not sure what to say, you could say this prayer:

> Jesus, thank you that you love me as my friend. Thank you that you died on the cross as my Saviour and came alive again for me. Jesus, you are my Lord and I want to follow you. Thank you that your Holy Spirit will help me to do this for ever. Amen.

The **best** bits

The funniest bit:

The silliest bit:

The bit I wanted to go on longer:

What I learned about God:

What I will remember most:

What I want to do next:

The **Scientists** in my **Lab!**

On these pages, collect the names, messages and doodles of the Scientists at the club and in your Lab. Remember your Researchers and Lab Technicians too!

If these materials have inspired you to wonder, head to www.faradaykids.com for the chance to explore more about science, faith, and what God has made.

The **answers!**

Page 19

Page 27

1 Koala
2 Leopard slug
3 Domestic cat
4 Great horned owl
5 Clown or anemone fish
6 Cockerel

Page 40

Question 1:

A NaCl is sodium chloride commonly known as salt.
B H2o is water
C C is carbon
D NaHCO3 is sodium bicarbonate otherwise known as baking soda

Question 2: Pluto

Question 3: Iris is the coloured part of your eye

Question 4:

A Zebra
B Tiger
C Giraffe
D Elephant

Question 5: Alexa (Amazon), Siri (Apple), Cortana (Microsoft), Watson (IBM) are among some of the best known but there are many others.

Credits
Page 25: Prehistoric fish by Matteo De Stefano/MUSE. Used under the Creative Commons Attribution-Share Alike 3.0 Unported licence: https://creativecommons.org/licenses/by-sa/3.0/deed.en